Arts Council of Great Britain

Ivory Carvings in
Early Medieval England
700-1200

8th May to 7th July 1974

Victoria & Albert Museum
London

Designed by

Trilokesh Mukherjee

Printed by

Shenval Press Harlow & London

Published by

The Arts Council of Great Britain

Acknowledgements

Roy Strong
Director
Victoria and Albert Museum

Robin Campbell
Director of Art
Arts Council of Great Britain

This exhibition was arranged at the suggestion of Lord Clark and arose from his admiration for John Beckwith's book on early English ivory carvings. It is rare indeed that the ideal exhibition can be realized; this is one of those occasions. Practically all the surviving works carved in ivory and bone during this long period of the early Middle Ages in England are here, thanks to the extraordinary generosity of those who own these precious objects. Our thanks must go first to the Metropolitan Museum in New York and its Director, Mr T. Hoving, who agreed to lend the great Cross, called the Bury St Edmunds Cross, exhibited here with the Corpus of Christ which surely belongs with it and is lent by the Kunstindustrimuseet of Oslo, to whom our thanks are also due, as they are to all those lenders whose names appear on p. 4.

Mr Beckwith has based the catalogue on his book and the publishers, Messrs Harvey Miller, have kindly allowed us to reprint parts of the text and to make use of the photographs used to illustrate the book.

We are indebted to the Italian Institute for practical assistance and to the Association Française d'Action Artistique for extending their patronage to the exhibition.

Lenders

Introduction

John Beckwith

The exhibition begins with the Franks Casket (Catalogue No. 1) from the British Museum, rejoined for the first time since the early nineteenth century to the side panel from the Museo Nazionale at Florence. The iconography of the casket is a strange synthesis of the cult of Woden, the dominance of Rome and a Christian theophany accompanied by inscriptions in Latin characters and runes which do not necessarily explain the scenes to which they are adjacent. The style of the figures is equally runic and recalls Pictish monuments in Scotland dating probably from the eighth century; much of the animal style looks back to the Book of Durrow; but it is clear that the artist knew an illustrated Legend of Wayland the Smith, an illustrated Chronicle of the World – indeed, some such work is known to have been given to King Aldfrith of Northumbria by Ceolfrid, Abbot of Monkwearmouth (690–716) – and a representation of the Adoration of the Magi.

Nearby some Northumbrian and Anglian carvings have been assembled, no doubt for the first time in history, and although they reflect the aesthetic muddle of the age they indicate the hold that Christianity was gaining over the country since the arrival of St Augustine in Kent in 597. The Gandersheim casket (No. 2) from Brunswick is wholly barbaric in style, decorated with Celtic spirals reminiscent of the enamelled bronze hanging bowls found in various parts of England and an animal style which may be related to a group of manuscripts produced in southern England, chiefly Canterbury, and dating from the second half of the eighth century. The runic inscription, however, invokes the protection of the Virgin for Ely, and there seems little doubt that the casket was made to contain a Christian relic. Similar in style, the little plaque from Larling in south-west Norfolk (No. 3), now in the Castle Museum, Norwich, combines a representation of the Capitoline wolf suckling Romulus and Remus – an analogous scene occurs on the Franks Casket – and a wyvern, but originally there were four decorated panels divided by a cross with expanded arms. More monumental in scale the great Genoels-Elderen diptych (No. 4) from Brussels, attributed on palaeographical grounds to a Northumbrian workshop of the eighth century, presents a concept of the human form and a sense of space – so different from the Franks Casket – which only Italo-Byzantine models could have provided. The theme of Christ treading the beasts, which recurs quite often in early medieval art in England, has forerunners at Ruthwell and Bewcastle but these crosses probably represent an old Romano-British tradition whereas the diptych suggests a new look at the golden age of early Christian antiquity in the late fourth, fifth and sixth centuries and heralds the imminent Carolingian *renovatio* of the ninth century. The panels from the collections of the Victoria and Albert Museum (Nos. 5 and 7) and those from the Bayerisches National-museum, Munich (Nos. 6 and 8), closely related, show that quite complex Christian imagery was current in England at the time: the Last Judgement scene

Introduction

is the first known in the West and the Ascension theme, if it is the Ascension, is certainly an early example; the latter is framed by insular ornament almost identical with that on the second small panel (No. 7) from the Victoria and Albert Museum. The style should be compared with the cross at South Church, St Andrew, Auckland, Co Durham, the cross at Rothbury, stone carvings at Breedon-on-the-Hill, and with a group of manuscripts produced at Jarrow and Canterbury. But this strange eclectic culture nearly foundered under the impact of the Viking invasions in the late eighth and the first half of the ninth century. In spite of the courage and wisdom of King Alfred (871–899), the patronage of his grandsons Athelstan (925–939) and Eadred (946–955), the revival of Anglo-Saxon culture made little headway until the providential appearance of three church men: St Dunstan, St Aethelwold and St Oswald. These three great men revived the Church, refounded monasteries based on the reformed Rule of St Benedict, and fostered the arts. They were, of course, firmly supported by King Edgar (959–975). From 960 onwards there was an increased production of illuminated manuscripts written in a reformed script and decorated in the so-called 'Winchester' style. No doubt the style originated in Winchester, an important bishopric and repository of the royal treasure, but it was not confined to that centre and in any case the whole aesthetic flowering was seeded from the Carolingian court workshops of the preceding century: the court art of Charlemagne, of his grandson Charles the Bald, the production of manuscripts, metalwork and ivory carvings from monasteries such as Fulda, Reims, Metz, Saint-Denis and Tours. Within this general stylistic movement there could, of course, be variations. On the one hand, for example, the dragon's head carved on the little spoon (No. 9), found recently at Winchester, reflects the style of the Bosworth Psalter (Brit. Mus. Add. Ms. 37517) probably written for St Dunstan in St Augustine's, Canterbury, possibly under his direction, although the calendar falls between 988, the year of Dunstan's death, and 1023; on the other hand the style of the carving of the Baptism of Christ on a small panel from a private collection in Paris (No. 10) and a Virgin and Child enthroned from the Ashmolean Museum, Oxford (No. 11) is greatly indebted to that of the Benedictional of St Aethelwold (Brit. Mus. Add. Ms. 49598) which was written and illuminated at the command of the saint in the period 971–984 either at the New Minster, Winchester, or at Ely. The panel of the Nativity from Liverpool (No. 21) follows closely an illumination in the Benedictional of St Aethelwold although it is slightly different in style from the preceding items. Again the cross reliquary from the Victoria and Albert Museum (No. 14) has been related to a Crucifixion scene in a psalter produced at Ramsey (Brit. Mus. Harley Ms. 2904) in the late tenth century but a small triangular panel carved with angels (No. 13) found near St Cross at Winchester echoes angels in a miniature commemorating King Edgar's presentation of a charter to the New Minister at Winchester in 966 (Brit. Mus. Cotton Ms. Vespasian A.viii). It must be remembered that the

Introduction

English houses were very closely related to each other.

The Carolingian workshops which seem to have exercised the greatest influence on the Anglo-Saxon artists appear to have been those of Reims and Metz, both important archbishoprics in the early middle ages: the framework of the miniatures in a manuscript like the Benedictional of St Aethelwold or the Pontifical produced at Winchester about 980 (Rouen, Bibliothèque municipale Ms.Y.7 (369)) seems to derive from Metz but the figure style depends in large part upon Reims. We know that a very important psalter, now known as the Utrecht Psalter, produced at Reims about 820, was in England by about the year 1000 since Canterbury monks were busy copying it for the next two centuries. The exact date of the arrival of this manuscript is not known. If the ivory chair of Charles the Bald, now in the Vatican, executed in the Metz style about 870–875, is any guidance the psalter was in the library of Charles the Bald in the middle of the ninth century and its removal from that library must have been by royal rather than by ecclesiastical instigation. It is possible that the psalter was brought over by Queen Aedgifu, sister of Athelstan and wife of Charles the Simple, King of the West Franks, after her husband's murder in 929. Aedgifu, with her son Louis d'Outremer, took refuge at the court of Athelstan and she brought with her at the time the Gandersheim Evangeliary, a manuscript produced at Metz about 860 with ivory covers now divided between the Herzogliche Sammlung, Veste Coburg and the Victoria and Albert Museum. She could have left the psalter with Athelstan and before his death in 939 he could have presented it to Canterbury. This is hypothesis but it is certain that the Reims style was current in England by the third quarter of the tenth century.

A small group of ivory carvings previously related to the Reims group, which has recently been recognised as the first court style of Charles the Bald, may well link up with the late tenth and early eleventh century copies of Reims manuscripts made in England. An ivory relief of the Transfiguration (No. 16) in the Victoria and Albert Museum, seems to be close in style to work done at Ramsey and Canterbury. The figures are larger in scale and less deeply undercut than the Carolingian carvings and the hunched figures of the Apostles recall the ecstatic collapse of St Pachomius receiving the Easter Tables in a manuscript written at Christ Church, Canterbury, in the first half of the eleventh century (Brit.Mus.Arundel Ms. 155, fol. 9v). A companion panel of the Ascension (No. 17) in the Victoria and Albert Museum, is carved in particularly low relief with drapery folds reminiscent of the stone carving of the Harrowing of Hell in Bristol Cathedral. With these panels should be considered the bookcovers in Paris (Bibl.Nat.lat.323) carved with a *Traditio Legis* (No. 18) and a Virgin and Child enthroned (No. 19) on which forms, gestures and draperies may be paralleled in a number of Anglo-Saxon manuscripts. Sometimes the forms of the

Introduction

Anglo-Saxon ivory carvings may be quite deeply undercut but they are always more monumental in scale than the Reims carvings of the previous century. The Virgin and St John the Evangelist from Saint-Omer (No. 20), the Christ in Majesty from the Metropolitan Museum, New York (No. 22), the Alcester tau-cross from the British Museum (No. 23), presenting another Christ treading the beasts, the vesica panels carved with Christ in Majesty and the Virgin and Child enthroned from the Victoria and Albert Museum (Nos. 24 and 25), even Godwine's seal from the British Museum (No. 26) all share the same characteristics: a lightness of poise, dramatic gestures, drapery with agitated folds and crinkled edges and, in spite of their small scale, emanating great power.

There is often a literary element and a zest for caricature. The Last Judgement scene on the Lady Gunhild's Cross from Copenhagen (No. 27) with its caricature of Satan, recalls the little panel carved with the same scene (No. 5) dating from the eighth century, and the inscriptions on the cross remind one of a tradition harking back to Ruthwell and its quotation from the Dream of the Rood and reaching forward to Sibylla's Cross (No. 48) from the Louvre in the middle of the twelfth century and the great cross from New York (No. 61) some forty years later. The St John of Beverley crozier from Mr John Hunt's collection in Ireland (No. 28) would appear to derive its inspiration from Bede's Ecclesiastical History. The walrus ivory pectoral reliquary cross (No. 29) from the Victoria and Albert Museum, with its representation of Ishmael the Archer recalls the Ruthwell Cross and an illustration in Aelfric of Eynsham's Digest of the Heptateuch (Brit. Mus. Cotton, Claudius B. iv), a Canterbury manuscript from the second quarter of the eleventh century, and, for that matter, commentaries of St Jerome and St Augustine on St Paul's Epistle to the Galatians iv referring to Genesis xxi; both make the point that Isaac was a type of the New Testament while Ishmael was the type of the Old Testament. On the pectoral cross, however, the artist has substituted for Isaac the *Agnus Dei* and the symbols of the Evangelists. The pencase (No. 30) from the British Museum, found in London, is decorated in part with agricultural and calendar pictures reminiscent of similar calendar pictures in Brit. Mus. Cotton, Julius vi. and again in Aelfric's Digest of the Heptateuch. The theme of Man's constant struggle with the dark forces of Nature, so clearly stated on the ivory throne of Charles the Bald in the ninth century, is frequently adumbrated in Anglo-Saxon art and literature. Men are attacked by monsters or entangled in shrubbery as on the bone comb (No. 31), found in Wales and now on loan from the British Museum, the Anglo-Norman tau-cross (No. 34) from the Victoria and Albert Museum and the Gloucester candlestick in Room 43. At the same time there is an implication that benign forces will prevail whether it is Christ in Majesty surrounded by the symbols of the Evangelists but set in a flurry of foliage as on the Pierpont Morgan book-cover (No. 33) or the little box carved with a miracle

Introduction

of St Lawrence (No. 15) or, above all, the haunting beauty carved in whalebone of the vision of the Virgin and Child adored by the Magi set above a frieze of fighting beasts and monsters (No. 35). It is probable that the majority of these carvings was produced at Canterbury in the second half of the eleventh century.

With the coming of the Normans the Anglo-Saxon Church, which had never quite emerged from the Nordic forests and fens, could be more closely integrated within the Roman dominion. The wealth of England enabled vigorous Lombard and Norman prelates to build great new churches, abbeys and castles, but the craftsmen who provided the fittings of gold, ivory, embroidery and illuminated books showed remarkably little Norman influence. As in the past they looked to the court art of the Holy Roman Empire, to the workshops on the Rhine, the Meuse, to the monasteries on the north-east coast of France and Flanders for guidance but they were also very set in their ways. They went on copying the Carolingian manuscripts which were available and they developed their own native style until well into the twelfth century.

A change of style becomes most marked in the scriptorium of the abbey of St Albans. A Norman abbot built the new church and dedicated it in the presence of King Henry I, Queen Matilda and an assembly of the new aristocracy. Abbot Geoffrey of Maine (1119–1146) sponsored the great shrine of St Alban made by the goldsmith Anketil and the fine psalter destined for the Prioress of Markyate. The style of the psalter is much influenced by the German scriptoria of the tenth and eleventh centuries: elongated figures in tubes of drapery, faces almost entirely in profile, staring eyes, a sagging jaw-line and an occasional pursed lip. The little box from the Victoria and Albert Museum carved with a pair of centaurs and two men mounted on lions (No. 37) is typical of the St Albans production, as indeed are two liturgical combs, one from a private collection in England (No. 38), the other from Verdun (No. 36), two prophets or kings (Nos. 39 and 40), one from the British Museum, the other from Lichfield, and a bobbin (No. 41) found recently in the keep of Norwich Castle.

The Vernon portable altar (No. 42) from the British Museum is carved in a different idiom and its style has been compared cogently with the sculpture added by Bishop Alexander (1123–48) to the west front of Lincoln Cathedral. A narwhal horn (No. 43) from the Victoria and Albert Museum, carved with spirals of foliate scrolls and panels of foliage inhabited by mannikins and monsters echoes the style of the sculpture on the portals of Lincoln Cathedral. On the other hand, a small Virgin and Child and a Magus (Nos. 44 and 45), the latter found in Dorset, come closer to sculptured reliefs in Dorset stone in Chichester Cathedral, and it seems likely that the Cross of Sibylla from the Louvre (No. 48) and two panels from Florence (Nos. 46 and 47), one carved

Introduction

with a representation of Christ treading the beasts and the other with St Michael spearing a very English devil, were produced in the west country. Further west still another style was prevalent in the middle of the twelfth century. An ivory relief of the Deposition from the Victoria and Albert Museum (No. 49) bears all the characteristics of sculpture at Kilpeck, Leominster and Castle Frome, a door knocker at Dormington and manuscripts in the cathedral library at Hereford.

At Winchester the old Anglo-Saxon traditions held faster but it is evident from the Psalter of St Swithun's (Brit. Mus. Cotton, Nero C IV) and the great Winchester Bible that new stylistic elements were in the air and this is reflected in the bone and ivory carvings produced in the monastic workshops: two book-covers (No. 50), possibly from the Shaftesbury Psalter (Brit. Mus. Lansdowne 383), a tau-cross (No. 51), a stool-arm (No. 52) and a crozier from Florence (No. 54) and another crozier from Paris (No. 53). The themes are much the same as they were in the eleventh century: men and monsters entangled in interlace and foliage, men attacked by dragons, the old 'Metz' intertwining foliage, but the forms have acquired a new solidity, an athletic vigour and a force of expression quite different from the Anglo-Saxon predecessors.

At Canterbury the Utrecht Psalter was still being copied about 1190 (Paris, Bibl. Nat. lat. 8846) but in a very different idiom from that of Brit. Mus. Harley Ms. 603 in the eleventh century or of Eadwine's Psalter (Cambridge, Trinity College Ms. R.17.1) about 1147. A small group of ivory carvings may be attributed to a Canterbury workshop between 1170 and 1190. An intricately carved crozier head (No. 55) with scenes from the life of St Nicholas and scenes from the Nativity, probably from the tomb of Archbishop Richard of Canterbury (1173–84), a small panel (No. 56) carved with the Ascension by an artist who appears to have been familiar with one of the earlier copies of the Utrecht Psalter, probably Harley Ms. 603, a small group representing the Rest on the Flight into Egypt from the Metropolitan Museum, New York (No. 57), a little capital carved with salamanders and mannikins (No. 58) from the British Museum, a torso of Christ from the Guildhall Museum (No. 60), Aaron's Rod from Florence (No. 63), and possibly a panel decorated with scenes of Biblical offering and sacrifice (No. 59) from Liverpool. But the most splendid candidate of all, though it has been previously assigned to Bury St Edmunds, may well be the great cross (Nos. 61 and 62) from the Metropolitan Museum, New York, carved with an astonishing complexity of Christian imagery and a wealth of inscriptions providing an anthology of prophetic and evangelistic texts and a consummation of mannerisms – the knotted cross, twisted heads, bulging eyes, expressive gestures, dancing postures – so familiar to the student of early medieval art in England.

General note

from: John Beckwith
Ivory Carvings in Early Medieval England
London 1972, p. 116.

From early times ivory was highly prized as an article of luxury. The combination of fine grain, soft colour and smooth texture made it a material easy to work upon with a minimum of sharp instruments – a knife, an awl, perhaps a fine drill – and it was easy to polish. It responded acceptably to pigmentation and it looked well in a setting of gold, precious stones and enamels. Cedar-wood furniture was frequently inlaid with ivory but the material could be adapted in various ways. Carvings in ivory were produced as statuettes of Divinity, as imperial and consular diptychs announcing the attainment of office, as religious diptychs with 'the commemoration of the living' and 'the commemoration of the dead' on the back and often used by the Orthodox Church as an instrument of ecclesiastical venom. Carvings in ivory were made up into chairs of state, into portable altars, into buckets for holy water; they were used as sceptres, as reliquaries in the form of a box or in the form of a cross, as receptacles for scent or jewellery; they sometimes expressed suffrages for the imperial welfare, announced a marriage or a moment of imperial autocracy; they were used as gifts in the course of religious and political diplomacy; they served as ambassadors of style and iconography.

In early times the tusk of the elephant was almost invariably used; most ivory carvings produced in the ancient Near East, in the Hellenistic and Graeco-Roman period, in Byzantine and early Islamic workshops were indebted to the elephant hunter operating chiefly in Africa. But with the collapse of the Roman Empire in the West, northern Europe was cut off from the old trade routes and since ivory was still so highly prized the northern peoples made use of the walrus tusk, the horn of a narwhal, the bone of the whale, or the bone of more domestic animals. Most ivory carvings produced in England in the early medieval period are of this category. Sometimes an ancient diptych was recarved but this is comparatively rare. Not until the twelfth century could northern workshops count on the import of elephant ivory and, no doubt, the main intermediary sources were Spain and Sicily. From that time onwards its use is fairly constant throughout the West.

Those exhibits illustrated actual size are marked with an asterisk (*).

Chronological Table

AD	English History
597	St. Augustine's mission from Rome arrives in Kent.
613–664	The Synod of Whitby establishes the supremacy of the Roman Church over the Celtic Church in England,
c 698	The Lindisfarne Gospels written and illuminated.
731	Bede finishes his major historical work, the 'Historia Ecclesiastica'.
793	The Vikings raid the Northumbrian coast and destroy the Church of Lindisfarne.
865	Major Viking invasion.
878	King Alfred's victory over the Vikings at Edington.
903	The consecration of King Edward's New Minster at Winchester.
940	St. Dunstan becomes Abbot of Glastonbury.
960	St. Dunstan is made Archbishop of Canterbury by King Edgar.
961	St. Oswald becomes Bishop of Worcester, and from 972-92 Archbishop of York.
963–84	St. Aethelwold Bishop of Winchester.
c 998	Aelfric writes his Anglo-Saxon paraphrase of the Heptateuch.
1016	Cnut the Dane becomes King of England.
1066	William the Conqueror, Duke of Normandy, invades England.
1086	The compilation of Domesday Book.
1093–1109	St. Anselm Archbishop of Canterbury.
1115	Consecration of St. Albans Abbey.
1129–71	Henry of Blois, Abbot of Glastonbury, holds the see of Winchester.
1133	Completion of Durham Cathedral.
1147–67	St. Ailred Abbot of Rievaulx.
1170	The murder of Thomas Becket, Archbishop of Canterbury.
1189	King Richard leaves on the third Crusade.

AD	Continental History
c 678	St. Wilfrid, Bishop of York, goes to Rome to plead for the restoration of his see.
696	The Anglo-Saxon missionary, St. Willibrord becomes Archbishop of Utrecht.
752	St. Boniface crowns Peppin King of the Franks.
800	Charlemagne, King of the Franks, is crowned Roman Emperor by the Pope.
853	The monastery of Tours destroyed by the Vikings.
877	The death of Charles the Bald, King of the Franks and Roman Emperor.
910	The foundation of the monastery of Cluny.
911	Rollo the Viking becomes first Duke of Normandy.
962	Otto I, King of Germany, is crowned Holy Roman Emperor.
1091	The Normans' final victory in the conquest of Sicily.
1097	The first Crusade arrives in the Holy Land.
1097	The foundation of the Abbey of Citeaux.
1115–53	St. Bernard Abbot of Clairvaux.
1144	The consecration of Abbot Suger's church of St. Denis.
1147	Beginning of the second Crusade.
1154–9	Nicholas Brakespear of St. Albans reigns as Pope Hadrian IV.

Bibliography

J. J. G. Alexander and
C. M. Kauffmann

*English Illuminated Manuscripts
700–1500,*
Brussels, Bibliothèque
Royale Albert 1er, Catalogue, 1973

M. Alexander

The Earliest English Poems
Penguin Classics 1967
Beowulf
Penguin Classics 1973

T. S. R. Boase

English Art 1100–1216
Oxford 1953
The York Psalter
London 1962

Christopher Brooke

From Alfred to Henry III 871–1272
(3rd impression) London, 1974

C. R. Dodwell

*The Canterbury School of Illumination
1066–1200*
Cambridge
The Great Lambeth Bible London 1939

C. M. Kauffmann

'*The Bury Bible*' (Cambridge,
Corpus Christi College Ms.2)
*Journal of the Warburg and Courtauld
Institutes* XXIX, 1966

T. D. Kendrick

Anglo-Saxon Art to A.D. 900
London 1938
Late Saxon and Viking Art
London 1949

D. Knowles

The Monastic Order in England
2nd edition Cambridge 1963

O. Pächt, C. R. Dodwell and
F. Wormald

The St Albans Psalter
London 1960

F. Saxl	*English Sculptures of the Twelfth Century* London 1954
R. W. Southern	*Western Society and the Church in the Middle Ages* Pelican, History of the Church II, London 1970
F. M. Stenton	*Anglo-Saxon England* Oxford 1943
H. Swarzenski	*Monuments of Romanesque Art* 2nd edition, London 1967
D. Talbot Rice	*English Art 871–1100* Oxford 1952
D. M. Wilson and O. Klindt-Jensen	*Viking Art* London 1966
F. Wormald	*English Drawings of the Tenth and Eleventh Centuries* London 1952 *The Benedictional of St Ethelwold* London 1959
G. Zarnecki	*English Romanesque Sculpture 1066–1140* London 1951 *Later English Romanesque Sculpture 1140–1210* London 1953

1

The Franks Casket

Whalebone

Northumbrian; about 700

h 10·5 cm l 23 cm w 18·5 cm

British Museum, London
and Museo Nazionale, Florence

John Beckwith, *Ivory Carvings in Early Medieval England* London, 1972, Catalogue No. 1; A. Becker, *Franks Casket. Zu den Bildern und Inschriften des Runenkästchen von Auzon.* Sprache und Literatur, Regensburger Arbeiten zur Anglistik und Amerikanistik (ed. K. H. Göller), Band 5, Regensburg, 1973.

On the lid an archer, identified as Egil in runes, defends his house against a body of armed men. Egil was the brother of Wayland the Smith; the woman seated behind him is possibly his wife Olrun, possibly a Valkyrie. The plain disc in the centre was probably covered by a metal plate with a handle. On the front are two scenes: on the right, the Adoration of the Magi, identified by runes; on the left

another scene from the story of
Wayland the Smith, usually identified
as Wayland holding the head of one of
King Nithhad's sons over an anvil, the
headless body lying below. Opposite,
followed by an attendant, is
Beaduhild, the king's daughter,
bringing a jewel to be mended;
alternatively, the attendant is also
Beaduhild bearing the bottle of
drugged beer which she will drink, fall
in a stupor, and then be raped by
Wayland. Behind is Egil catching birds
in order that Wayland might make
wings from the feathers; alternatively,
the archer is one of the sons of King
Nithhad whom Wayland was using as
an accessory for his revenge. The runes
surrounding these scenes have been
variously read; the most plausible
translation seems to be 'the fish-flood

(sea) lifted the whale's bones on to the steep shore; the ocean became turbid where he swam aground on the shingle'.

On the left end are represented Romulus and Remus in a wood suckled by a wolf; above is a second wolf and, on either side, two men armed with spears. The inscription in runes may be rendered 'far from their native land Romulus and Remus, two brothers; a she-wolf nourished them in Rome city'. On the back the inscription is partly in runes and partly in Latin: 'here the inhabitants escape from Jerusalem' and 'here are fighting Titus and the Jews'. The runes in the lower corners probably mean 'judgement' and 'hostage'. The subject is the capture of Jerusalem by Titus in 70 AD who is perhaps represented in the upper scene to the left holding a sword; to the right are Jews in flight; below, to the left is a judgement scene, to the right a group of hostages. It has been suggested that the central building is the temple containing the Ark of the Covenant, with the oxen below the sea of brass, and the cherubim (I Kings, vii, 44). On the right side is a much disputed scene which some have connected with the Siegfried Saga, but it seems probable that the death of a hero attended by Valkyries is represented. The runes are equally obscure. A plausible translation seems to be 'here (she) sits on the sorrow-hill, endures tribulation imposed on her, rendered wretched by sorrow and anguish of heart'.

Formerly in the church of Saint-Julien at Brioude (Haute Loire) the casket early in the nineteenth century was in the possession of a family at Auzon, near Brioude, where it was used as a work-box. Later the silver mounts were removed, the casket fell apart and one side got mislaid. The top and remaining sides were acquired by Professor Mathieu of Clermont-Ferrand, then bought by a Parisian dealer who sold them in 1857 to Sir A. W. Franks who in turn presented them in 1867 to the British Museum. The missing side was found at Auzon and bought by M. Carrand of Lyons, who bequeathed it with his collection to the Museo Nazionale at Florence.

The casket has been much discussed, usually from the philological side. The combination of runes and Latin lettering is found on other Northumbrian monuments of a slightly earlier date, such as the wooden coffin of St Cuthbert (about 698), preserved in the Durham Cathedral Library and the Ruthwell Cross. The Romulus and Remus story is found on Anglo-Saxon sceattas (silver pennies) dating from the seventh or eighth century and on the Larling plaque (Cat. No. 3). For the reference to the sack of Jerusalem by Titus there seems little doubt that the model was an illustrated Chronicle of the World; some such work is known to have been given to King Aldfrith of Northumbria by Ceolfrid, Abbot of Wearmouth (690–716). The figure style and the general atmosphere of heroic combat may be found on Pictish monuments in Scotland dating from the eighth or ninth century.

2

The Gandersheim Casket

Bone panels with lock and mounts of bronze

Ely (?); late eighth century

h 12·6 cm l 12·6 cm w 6·8 cm

Herzog Anton Ulrich-Museum, Brunswick, Inv. No. MA 58

Beckwith, *op cit* no 2

On the bottom is a runic inscription which has been read 'Holy Virgin be thou a light to Ely'. The bronze base, however, is of later date than the bone panels.

Formerly at Gandersheim. After the secularisation of the convent in 1803 the casket with other things passed to the museum at Brunswick. Gandersheim is recorded to have relics of the Virgin's clothing. Scholars have observed the similarity in style between the animal ornament and interlace on the casket and that of a group of manuscripts of the second half of the eighth century, some of which can be localised at Canterbury and the remainder in the south of England. It has been generally agreed that from the runic inscription the origin of the casket at Ely, before the monastery was destroyed by the Danes in 886, may be inferred; all are agreed that a date in the late eighth century is probable.

3

The Larling Plaque

Bone. Fragment of a casket or a bookcover

Anglian; late eighth century

greatest *h* 2·55 cm *w* 7·2 cm

The Castle Museum, Norwich

Barbara Green, 'An Anglo-Saxon plaque from Larling, Norfolk', *Antiquaries Journal*, LI, 1971, pp 321 ff

In the centre was a raised rectangular panel with a plain border which was subdivided into four small rectangular panels by an expanded arm cross. On the lower left panel Romulus and Remus; on the right a wyvern.

Found in a daffodil field at Larling in south-west Norfolk, near the church dedicated to St Ethelbert, King of East Anglia, beheaded by Offa of Mercia in 794.

The plaque has been related to the Gandersheim casket (Cat. No. 2) and examples of Anglo-Saxon metalwork and stone crosses, in particular the Aldborough and Rothbury crosses, dating to the late eighth century. Reference has been made to the silver penny attributed to Ethelbert of East Anglia (d. 794) which bears 'a truly classical rendering' of Romulus and Remus in an Anglo-Saxon context. The East Anglian royal house claimed descent from Caesar – a genealogy, like those of other royal houses, largely established in the late eighth century.

4

The Genoels-Elderen Diptych

Ivory, pierced

Northumbrian;
last quarter of the eighth century

each leaf: *h* 30 cm *w* 18 cm

Musées Royaux d'Art et d'Histoire
Brussels, no 1474

Beckwith, *op cit* no 3; P. Lasko,
Ars Sacra: 800–1200, Pelican History
of Art, 1972, p. 13

On the left leaf Christ treading the
beasts between angels. The Latin
inscription refers to Psalm 90 (91).13
and explains the scene.

On the right leaf two panels enclose the Annunciation and the Visitation identified by Latin inscriptions.

Most scholars have related this diptych to the Godescalc Evangelistary and to ivory carvings produced at the court of Charlemagne but the style is not of the court. Close relations with insular manuscripts have also been detected. The key to the diptych is surely provided by the St Andrew Auckland Cross, Co Durham, where a similar flatness of relief and stylisation of drapery prevail. The inscriptions, long recognised as having insular characteristics, have been identified as Northumbrian.

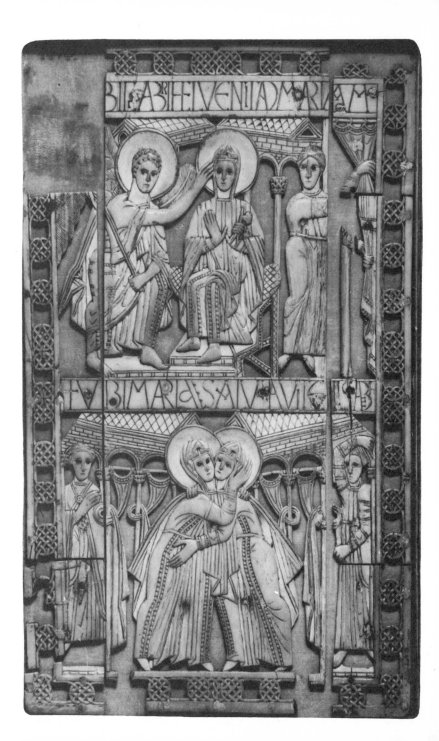

5

The Last Judgement*

Ivory

Anglo-Saxon;
late eighth or early ninth century

h 13·2 cm w 8·1 cm

Victoria and Albert Museum, London
no 253–1867

Beckwith, *op cit* no 4

From the Webb Collection

The first representation of the Last
Judgement known in the West and
the first representation of Hades
swallowing the damned which was to
become remarkably constant in early
medieval English illumination and was
not adopted on the continent for a
considerable period of time. Birds,
representing souls, flying towards
corpses to signify resurrection,
occur on crosses in Ireland at
Clonmacnois and Durrow. The text of
the inscription (Matt. xxv, 34) is not
taken from the Vulgate but from the
Old Latin version of the Gospels.

6

Christ in Majesty★

Ivory

Anglo-Saxon; eighth century

h 10·2 cm w 9·8 cm

Bayerisches Nationalmuseum, Munich
no MA 158

Beckwith, *op cit* no 7

Possibly from an Ascension group

An old ivory diptych with the back
prepared for wax has been used.
Acquired in 1870 in Welschellen,
Post St Lorenzen (Pustertal, Tirol).

7

Decorative panel*

Ivory

Anglo-Saxon; late eighth century

h 13·2 cm w 8·1 cm

Victoria and Albert Museum, London
no 254–1867

Beckwith, *op cit* no 8

From the Webb Collection

8

The Ascension

Ivory

Anglo-Saxon; late eighth century

h 10·8 cm *w* 30·7 cm

Bayerisches Nationalmuseum, Munich
no MA 164

Beckwith, *op cit* no 9

The scene has also been identified as the Assumption. Probably once the side of a casket. It is possible that an old ivory diptych with its back prepared for wax has been used.

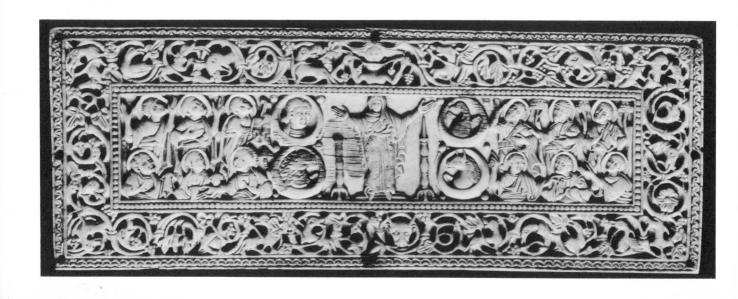

9

Fragment of a spoon

Ivory

Anglo-Saxon; late tenth century

h 5·9 cm greatest *w* 2·6 cm

Winchester City Museum

Beckwith, *op cit* no 10

Found in the excavations at the Old
and New Minster, Winchester.

10

The Baptism of Christ

Walrus ivory

Anglo-Saxon;
late tenth or early eleventh century

h 9 cm

Private collection, Paris

Beckwith, *op cit* no 14

Formerly in the Stanislas Baron
Collection, then Martin-Le-Roy, now
privately owned.

The style of the relief is closely related
to the illuminations in the Benedictional od St Aethelwold (British
Museum Add. Ms 49598) which was
produced at the command of the saint
in the period 971–984 either at the Old
Minster, Winchester, or at Ely, which
had been refounded by St Aethelwold,
Bishop of Winchester.

11

The Virgin and Child enthroned

Walrus ivory

Anglo-Saxon;
late tenth or early eleventh century

h 9·52 cm w 5·72 cm

Visitors of the Ashmolean Museum,
Oxford

Beckwith, *op cit* no 15

Formerly in the possession of the
Rev. Paul W. Wyatt, Bedford.

12

The Crucifixion★

Walrus ivory

Anglo-Saxon;
late tenth or early eleventh century

h 9·6 cm w 5·7 cm

Danish National Museum, Copenhagen
Inv no D 13324

Beckwith, *op cit* no 17a

From a private collection bequeathed
in 1944 to the Museum. As the
collection contained some items
labelled as 'earth finds from
Copenhagen' it is probable that the
relief was found during excavations in
the city.

13

Two Angels

Walrus ivory

Anglo-Saxon (Winchester?);
late tenth century

h 7·5 cm greatest w 5 cm

Winchester City Museum

Beckwith, *op cit* no 16

Possibly from a small casket or a
portable altar as part of a representation of Christ in Majesty.

Said to have been found in a garden
near St Cross at Winchester.

14

A Crucifix Reliquary

Walrus ivory mounted on gold with
gold filigree and cloisonné enamels
on a cedar wood core

Anglo-Saxon; late tenth century

h (of cross) 18·5 cm *w* 13·4 cm
h (of ivory) 12·5 cm *w* 11 cm

Victoria and Albert Museum, London
no M 7943–1862

Beckwith, *op cit* no 20

From the Webb Collection
Formerly in the Soltikoff Collection

The ivory figure covers a large cavity
for relics and it is possible that other
cavities exist under the enamel
medallions. The inscription, now
fragmentary, listed the relics formerly
contained in the cross, apparently
beginning with a relic of the True
Cross. The crown of thorns, if such it
is, is most unusual for this date. In an
inventory of gifts made by King
Athelstan (925–939) to the shrine of
St Cuthbert at Chester-le-Street
mention is made of a cross of gold and
ivory.

15

A Miracle of St Lawrence ?

Walrus ivory box

Anglo-Saxon; early eleventh century

h 6·5 cm *w* 6 cm

Victoria and Albert Museum, London
no 268–1867

Beckwith, *op cit* no 19

From the Webb Collection

The late Lady Cox (M. D. Anderson)
suggested verbally that the scenes may
refer to a miracle of St Lawrence as
related by Jacopo de Voragine, *The
Golden Legend*, London, 1900, IV,
p. 218.

'In the church of St Laurence at Milan
was a chalice of crystal marvellously
clear, and as the deacon bare it

suddenly to the altar, it fell out of his hands to the ground and was all to-broken. And then the deacon, weeping, gathered together the pieces and laid them on the altar, and prayed the holy martyr St Laurence that the chalice might be made whole again, and then anon it was founden all whole.' There are certain details in the story which are not illustrated on the box but the main outlines seem to tally.

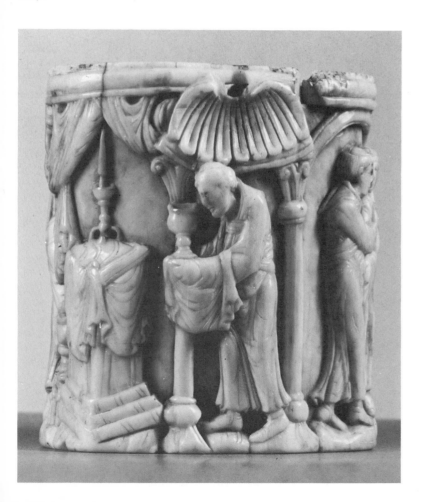

16

The Transfiguration★

Ivory

Anglo-Saxon; late tenth century

On the other side, the Last Judgement, cf no 5

h 13·2 cm *w* 8·1 cm

Victoria and Albert Museum, London no 253–1867

Beckwith, *op cit* no 21

From the Webb Collection

Previously related to Reims production in the ninth century this relief and its companion (No 17) and a book-cover in Paris (No. 18–19) may well be associated with copies of Reims manuscripts made in England in the late tenth and eleventh century.

17

The Ascension★

Ivory

Anglo-Saxon; late tenth century

h 13·2 cm *w* 8·1 cm

Victoria and Albert Museum, London
no 254–1867

Beckwith, *op cit* no 22

From the Webb Collection

On the other side, panels of insular
ornament, cf, No. 7.

18

Traditio Legis★

Ivory

Anglo-Saxon; late tenth century

h 15·8 cm   w 11·13 cm

Bibliothèque Nationale, Cabinet des
Manuscrits, Paris
Cod lat 323

Beckwith, *op cit* no 23

The relief is mounted in a late Gothic
silver frame and attached to a modern
black leather binding. The manuscript
is an Evangelistary dating from the
middle of the ninth century formerly
belonging to the Maréchal de Noailles.

19

The Virgin and Child enthroned★

Ivory

Anglo-Saxon; late tenth century

h 15·4 cm *w* 11 cm

Bibliothèque Nationale, Cabinet des
Manuscrits, Paris
Cod lat 323

Beckwith, *op cit* no 24

20

The Virgin and St John the Evangelist*

Walrus ivory

Anglo-Saxon;
late tenth or early eleventh century

h 12·5 cm in both cases

Musée Hotel Sandelin, Saint-Omer
No 2822

Beckwith, *op cit* no 25

In both figures the eyes are inlaid with black beads, perhaps of jet.

From a group of the Crucifixion.

Said to have come from the Abbey of Saint-Bertin at Saint-Omer.

21

The Nativity

Walrus ivory

Anglo-Saxon;
late tenth or early eleventh century

h 8 cm   *w* 6·5 cm

Merseyside County Museums,
Liverpool
no M8060

Beckwith, *op cit* no 26

Formerly in the Mayer Collection;
previously in the collection of Mr
Rolfe at Sandwich

The style and composition parallel
closely a miniature of the same scene
in the Benedictional of St Aethelwold,
Brit.Mus.Add. Ms.49598, fol. 15b.

22

Christic in Majesty on the back
**the Agnus Dei with the symbols
of St John the Evangelist
and St Luke**★

Walrus ivory

Anglo-Saxon; early eleventh century

h 15·5 cm   w 6·5 cm

The Metropolitan Museum of Art,
New York, Gift of
J. Pierpont Morgan

Beckwith, *op cit* no 27

Possibly from the Abbey of
Saint-Bertin at Saint-Omer

Both sides of the original quatrefoil
design broken away. Several holes for
gold plating; traces of red pigmentation on the eagle.

Formerly in the Pierpont Morgan
Collection; previously in the Charles
Mannheim Collection, Paris, and
before that in the Quinson Collection,
Saint-Omer and Arras.

23

The Alcester Tau-Cross

Walrus ivory

Anglo-Saxon; early eleventh century

l 14·5 cm

British Museum, London

Beckwith, *op cit* no 29

On one side Christ on the Cross; on the other Christ treading the beasts.

The outer edges of the volutes are pierced with small holes as if for the insertion of pearls or other jewels. Traces of gilding in several places.

Found in the Rectory garden at Alcester, Warwickshire, and possibly formerly at Evesham Abbey, founded in Saxon times.

Given by the Friends of the British Museum (afterwards the National Art-Collections Fund) in 1903

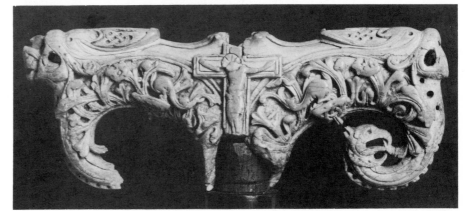

24

Christ in Majesty★

Walrus ivory

Anglo-Saxon; early eleventh century

h 9·5 cm

Victoria and Albert Museum, London
no A 32–1928

Beckwith, *op cit* no 39

A portion of the background and
border on the left side has been broken
and restored in plaster. Originally gold
plated.

Acquired in London.

25

The Virgin and Child enthroned★

Walrus ivory

Anglo-Saxon; early eleventh century

h 10 cm w 6·67 cm

Victoria and Albert Museum, London
no A 5–1935

Beckwith, *op cit* no 40

Several holes in the border suggest
gold plating.
It seems likely that this relief and
No 24, though different in style, are
companion pieces and may have come
from a bookcover.

Given by Monsieur Alphonse Kann
who acquired it from Demotte.

26

Godwine's Seal

Walrus ivory

Anglo-Saxon;
late tenth or early eleventh century

h 8·5 cm; diameter of disc 4·44 cm

British Museum, London

Beckwith, *op cit* no 41

The handle is carved in high relief with God the Father and God the Son seated upon a throne with their feet resting upon a naked prostrate man. A small piece is broken away from the top and there are indications that on this the Holy Ghost in the form of a dove was represented. The Latin inscriptions, which include Anglo-Saxon letters, refer to a Godwine 'minister' and to a nun Godgytha. It seems likely that Godwine was the founder of a religious house and Godgytha was abbess.

There was a Saxon monastery at Cholsey, near Wallingford, said to have been founded by Aethelred and destroyed by the Danes in 1006. A Godwine 'minister' witnessed numerous charters in the reign of Aethelred between 980 and 1016.

Found with a whetstone and a small plain ivory double comb in a garden on the west side of the market place at Wallingford, Berks.

Given by Sir A. W. Franks in 1881.

27

The Lady Gunhild's Cross

Walrus ivory

Anglo-Saxon (?); about 1075

h 28·5 cm *w* 22 cm thickness 2·5 cm

Danish National Museum, Copenhagen
no 9087

Beckwith, *op cit* no 43; Lasko,
Ars Sacra, p. 168

The figure of Christ is missing from
the front of the cross leaving only a
cross-haloed nimbus and the inscription above identifying Jesus of
Nazareth, King of the Jews. At the
ends of the arms of the cross are
personifications of Life and Death, the
Church and the Synagogue. On the
back of the cross, the Last Judgement
with Latin inscriptions referring to the
scene. Further inscriptions on the
sides of the cross refer to Helena,
daughter of the King of Sweden, to the
fact that Liutger ordered the cross to
be made at the request of Helena who
was also known as Gunhild, the latter
name in runes.

There are traces of red, green and gold
pigmentation and it is possible that the
cross was plated with gold. The eyes
were beaded with jet.

The cross belonged to Sophie Brahe (d.
1646), widow of Holger Rosenkrantz.
Helena, otherwise known as Gunhild,

was the daughter of King Swend Estridson, and therefore great-niece of King Cnut the Great of England; she died in 1074 or 1076. A certain Liutger is known to have been canon of Lund before the second half of the twelfth century. It is not impossible that an artist with this name should be English and it has been pointed out that whatever the nationality he was strongly influenced by English work which had a high reputation on the continent at this time. In the second half of the eleventh century the Danes carried away with them a quantity of treasure and relics from the abbeys of Ely and Peterborough; some of this was brought back to the country, but a part seems to have remained in Denmark. The cross is a complex

structure on which the inscriptions
are almost as important from the
point of view of ornament as the
decoration – a 'literary' cross looking
back to the Ruthwell Cross with its
extract from *The Dream of the Rood*
and forward to the ivory cross of
Sibylla (No 48), and the so-called
Bury St Edmunds cross (No 61). The
shape of the Omega on the book in the
lap of Christ in the scene of the Last
Judgement occurs on ivory carvings
which may well be English but also of
twelfth century date (cf. Nos 46, 49).
In the roundel containing the damned
the devil and his companions are
depicted in characteristic Anglo-Saxon
caricature. The figures on the left arm
of the cross recall a Judgement of
Solomon on a capital in Westminster
Abbey which has been assigned to the
early twelfth century but may well be
earlier. Art in Viking Denmark
provides no kind of analogy and it
seems reasonable to suppose that the
cross was exported from England
whose aristic influence was pre-
ponderant in Scandinavia about this
time.

28

The St John of Beverley Crozier

Walrus ivory

Anglo-Saxon,
middle of the eleventh century

h 9·5 cm greatest w 6·5 cm

Mr John Hunt,

Beckwith, *op cit* no 44 and cf pp 59–60

On one side St John of Beverley (d. 721), identified by an inscription, cures a dumb youth by blessing him with the deacon Berethun as witness. On the other side, St Peter, holding a cross staff, attended by St John the Evangelist, both identified by inscriptions, cures a lame man in the Temple.

Bede (*Ecclesiastical History*, V, ii) recounts the miracle of St John of Beverley which occurred in 685 and relates it to a miracle of St Peter and St John who cured a cripple in the Temple (Acts III, 5). The late Francis Wormald identified the inscription referring to St John of Beverley and suggested that the scene on the reverse might be a Harrowing of Hell. In the first scene Mr John Hunt preferred to identify Berethun as St. Peter holding a key and to read the latter scene as Christ represented as the Good Samaritan but the fact that the Apostles are named on the crozier in connection with the scene suggests that Bede's account provides the key to both sides. St John of Beverley, Bishop of Hexham (686–705), Archbishop of York (705–717) was educated at Canterbury by Archbishop Theodore. He lived for a time at Whitby under the Abbess Hild and is said to have taught Bede and certainly ordained him. He was not canonised until 1037 when the relics were translated from York to Beverley. There was a second translation after a fire in 1197. The remains were discovered in 1664 and reburied in the nave of the minster; they were again brought to light in 1736.

29

Pectoral Cross

Walrus ivory

Anglo-Saxon (Canterbury?);
about 1100

h 11·92 cm; *w* 4·62 cm; *d* 2·7 cm

Victoria and Albert Museum, London
no A-6-1966
Beckwith, *op cit* no 45

The cross is a small box carved and
pierced in low relief to form a case for
an inner gold box (now lost) which
would have contained a relic, possibly
a relic of the True Cross. On the lid an
archer aiming at a bird, probably
Ishmael, the son of Abraham and

Hagar; on the bottom of the box (or
the back of the cross) the *Agnus Dei*
and the symbols of the Evangelists.
The style of the carving has been
compared with Canterbury illuminations and drawings dating from the
eleventh and early twelfth century and
with various ivory carvings (Nos 30 to
33) ranging in date from the middle
of the eleventh to the early twelfth
century.

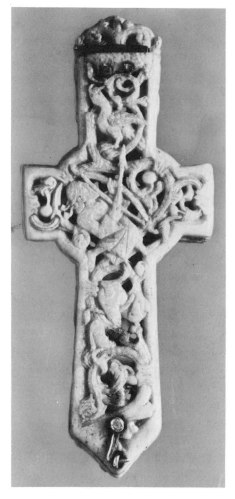

30

Pen-case

Walrus ivory

Anglo-Saxon;
middle of the eleventh century

l 23·5 cm

British Museum, London

Beckwith, *op cit* no 46

Found in the City of London and
acquired in 1870.

The agricultural and hunting scenes
recall certain calendar pictures in
British Museum, Cotton, Julius
A. VI, fol 3b and Tiberius B. V. fol. 3
and 7 and Aelfric's Heptateuch,
Claudius B. IV. fol. 61 b.

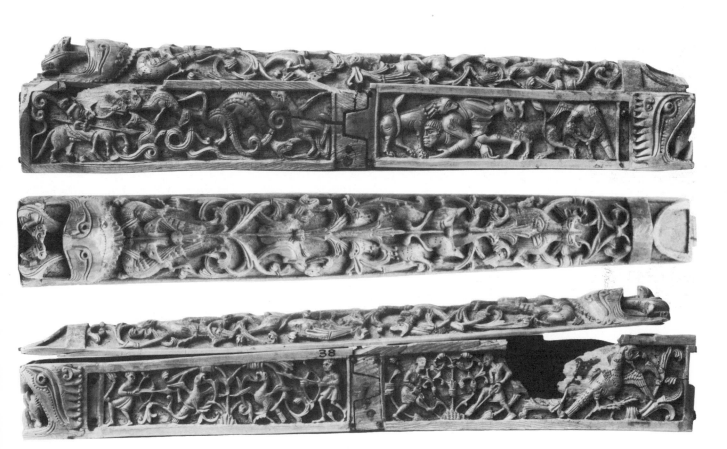

31

Liturgical comb

Bone

Anglo-Saxon;
late eleventh or early twelfth century

l 22 cm

British Museum, London

Beckwith, *op cit* no 47

Found in Wales. Acquired in 1856
from the Maskell Collection.

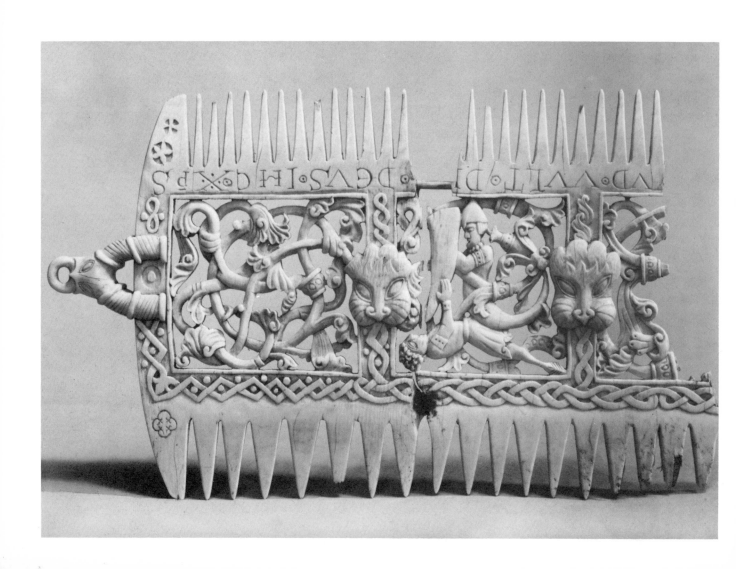

32

Pierced panel from a casket*

Walrus ivory

Anglo-Saxon;
late eleventh or early twelfth century

h 6·6 cm l 18·4 cm

Musée de Cluny, Paris
no 1050

Beckwith, *op cit* no 48

Several holes in the borders suggest
that the casket was originally plated in
gold.

33

Christ in Majesty

Ivory, pierced

Anglo-Saxon (?);
late eleventh century

h 11·0 cm w 9·5 cm

Pierpont Morgan Library, New York
Ms. 319

Beckwith, *op cit* no 49

On the cover of a Gospel Book of
Marchiennes, Franco-Flemish, dating
to the first half of the tenth century.
The leather binding of Ms. 319,
formerly in the library of Prince
Baucina of Rome, dates from the
seventeenth century; the ivory relief
previously ascribed to a North French
or Belgian workshop of the tenth or
eleventh century, is inset but has no
relationship with the style of the
illuminations.

34

Head of a Tau-Cross

Walrus ivory

Anglo-Norman;
late eleventh or early twelfth century

h 4·5 cm w 14·5 cm

Victoria and Albert Museum, London
no 372–1871

Beckwith, *op cit* nos 58 and 59

From the Webb Collection. In 1806
the head of the tau-cross was in the
possession of Mgr. de Clermont at
Le Mans

The carving would appear to be by the
same hand that carved part of a pierced
walrus ivory panel, now in the British
Museum, found on the site of the
infirmary of the abbey of St Albans
during excavations in 1920.

35

The Adoration of the Magi

Whalebone

Anglo-Norman; late eleventh century

h 36·5 cm Greatest width 16 cm

Victoria and Albert Museum, London
no 142–1866

Beckwith, *op cit* no 63; Lasko, *Ars Sacra*, p. 172, prefers a Flemish centre, possibly Saint-Omer, but the English influence on the scriptorium of Saint-Omer is well known.

From the Webb Collection
Formerly in the Soltikoff Collection

In the past the relief has been assigned to a provenance ranging from Spain to Scandinavia, but considering the material in which it is carved and the close similarities with Anglo-Saxon and Norman manuscripts, with wall-paintings at Clayton dating from the end of the eleventh century, and affinities with Norman architecture and Anglo-Saxon ivory carvings, a workshop near the English Channel seems indicated.

36

Liturgical comb*

Ivory

English (School of St Albans);
about 1120

h 8·5 cm *w* 11·8 cm

Musée de la Princerie, Verdun

Beckwith, *op cit* no 66

On one side, the Last Supper, the
Betrayal and the Flagellation; above,
two angels, one holding a soul; below,
Judas and two angry figures, one
holding a book and the other pointing
to the text. On the other side, the
Entombment and sleeping soldiers,
the Maries at the Sepulchre with,
above, an angel swinging a thurible,
and below, Christ appearing to St
Mary Magdalene; on the ends two
dragons.

Formerly in the Cathedral of Verdun.
Inventories of the Cathedral Treasure
dating from 1745 and 1773 state that
the comb was a gift from the Emperor
Henry II (1002–1024) to Richard,
Abbot of Saint-Vannes, hence the
appellation 'comb of St Henry'.
Considering the style and date of the
comb, the owner or donor is more
likely to have been Henry, archdeacon
of Winchester, who became Bishop of
Verdun in 1117.

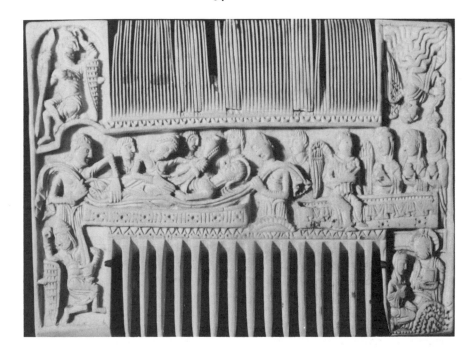

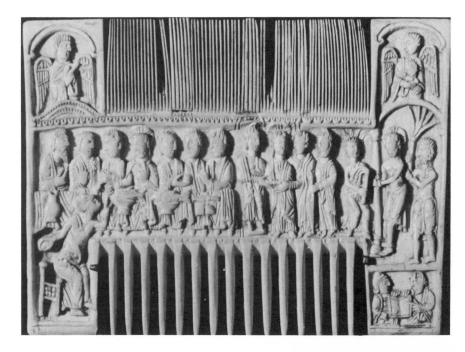

37

Oval box

Walrus ivory with silver mounts

English (School of St Albans);
about 1120
The silver mounts are modern

h 7·5 cm   *l* 6·5 cm   *w* 3·5 cm

Victoria and Albert Museum, London
no 208–1874

Beckwith, *op cit* no 64

From the Webb Collection
Formerly in the collection of
M. Le Carpentier

The style of this and other ivory carvings (cf. Nos. 38 to 41) has been related to manuscripts produced at St Albans and Bury St Edmunds between 1120 and 1150.

38

Liturgical Comb*

Ivory

English (School of St Albans);
about 1120

h 8·5 cm *l* 11·5 cm

Collection: Miss Olive Lloyd-Baker,
CBE JP

Beckwith, *op cit* no 65; Lasko, *Ars
Sacra*, p. 235

On one side, the Nativity, the Flight into Egypt, the Washing of the Feet of the Disciples, the Last Supper, the Betrayal, the Crucifixion and the Entombment; on the other, The Massacre of the Innocents, the Adoration of the Magi, the Departure of the Magi, and the Annunciation to the Shepherds; on the ends, a continuation of the Annunciation to the shepherds and the soldiers on guard at the Sepulchre.

39

A King or Prophet

Walrus ivory

English (School of St Albans);
second quarter of the twelfth century

h 10·8 cm *w* 3 cm

British Museum, London

Beckwith, *op cit* no 68; Lasko, *Ars Sacra*, p. 166 prefers a date in the late eleventh century

Probably from a portable altar. The eyes are inlaid with jet beads. Formerly in the Rohde Hawkins Collection. Acquired in 1885.

40

A King or Prophet

Walrus ivory

English (School of St Albans);
second quarter of the twelfth century

h 8 cm *w* 2·5 cm

By courtesy of the Dean and Chapter of Lichfield Cathedral

Beckwith, *op cit* no 69; Lasko, *Ars Sacra*, p. 166

Probably from a portable altar. The eyes are inlaid with jet beads.

41

Bobbin*

Walrus ivory

English (School of St Albans);
second quarter of the twelfth century

l 6·5 cm

Castle Museum, Norwich

Beckwith, 'A Romanesque Bobbin',
Intuition und Kunstwissenschaft.
Festschrift für Hanns Swarzenski,
Berlin, 1973, pp. 233 ff

Found in the basement of the keep of
Norwich Castle in October 1972.

42

Portable altar

Whalebone

English (Lincoln); second quarter of the twelfth century

h 8·2 cm *l* 23 cm *w* 15·2 cm

British Museum, London

Beckwith, *op cit* no 81; Lasko, *Ars Sacra*, p. 236

At one end Christ in Majesty flanked
by the symbols of the Evangelists; at
the other end, Christ on the Cross
between the Virgin and St John the
Evangelist; on the sides, the Twelve
Apostles. Traces of polychrome
decoration, particularly on the lips and
eyes of the Apostles.

Formerly in the collection of Lord
Vernon.

Exhibited at the Fine Arts Exhibition,
Derby, 1870.

The style of the carving has been
compared to the sculpture added to
the west front of Lincoln Cathedral by
Bishop Alexander between 1123 and
1146.

43

Ceremonial staff

Narwhal horn

English (possibly Lincoln);
second quarter of the twelfth century

l 117 cm

Victoria and Albert Museum, London
no A. 79–1936

Beckwith, *op cit* no 82

The horn was originally longer and it
has been broken and repaired in two
places. The pins on the plain surfaces
between the bands of ornament
suggest gold plating.

A second narwhal horn, similarly
carved, probably from the same workshop and of the same date, is in a
private collection in England.

The style of the carving has been
compared to sculpture on the portals
of Lincoln Cathedral.

Purchased under the bequest of
Capt. H. B. Murray.

44

The Virgin and Child*

Walrus ivory

English (Dorchester?);
middle of the twelfth century

_h_ 13·5 cm _w_ 6·35 cm

Victoria and Albert Museum, London
no A 25 – 1933

Beckwith, _op cit_ no 83

The figures were originally part of an
Adoration of the Magi, of which one
Magus survives (No. 45).

The eyes were inlaid with jet or glass
beads.
The style of the figures, including that
of the Magus, has been compared with
reliefs, carved in Dorset stone, in
Chichester Cathedral, probably by
sculptors from the county.

Purchased under the bequest of
Francis Reubell Ryan.

45

A Magus★

Walrus ivory

English (Dorchester?);
middle of the twelfth century

h 13 cm

Dorset National History and
Archeological Society, Dorset County
Museum, Dorchester

Beckwith, *op cit* no 84

The eyes are drilled but the jet or
glass beads are missing. The back is
plain but shaped evidently to fit into a
shallow groove in the background
to which it was attached by two ivory
or bone pins, the holes for which are
seen on the right side.

Found at Milborne St Andrews, near
Dorchester, probably in the first half
of the nineteenth century; the figure
then belonged to Mr C. Hall, of
Anstey, near Milborne, and was lent
in 1902 by his grandson, Mr C. L.
Hall, to the Dorset County Museum
which, a few years later, purchased it.

46

Christ treading the Beasts*

Walrus ivory

English; middle of the twelfth century

h 11·4 cm *w* 5·7 cm

Museo Nazionale, Florence
Carrand. No. 70

Beckwith, *op cit* no 85

The Latin inscription refers to Christ's
victory over Death as being compar-
able to His trampling the Lion and the
Serpent. The shape of the letter Omega
should be compared with that on
other ivories of a probable English
provenance (Nos. 27, 49).

At one time the left side of the panel
was joined to the right side of No. 47
by leather bands for which four holes
were drilled. Part of the staff is broken
away.

Formerly in the Charvet and Carrand
Collections.

47

St Michael trampling Satan★

Walrus ivory

English; middle of the twelfth century

h 11·4 cm *w* 5·7 cm

Museo Nazionale, Florence
Carrand. No. 71

Beckwith, *op cit* no 86

The Latin inscription states that St
Michael bearing the shield of Faith
dominates with his whole body the
prostrate enemy. The face of the
Archangel is much rubbed. Part of the
spear is broken away. Four holes at the
back were intended for leather bands
to connect with No. 46. The back of
the relief has been prepared for wax as
a writing tablet.

Formerly in the Charvet and Carrand
Collections

48

The Crucifix of Sibylla

Walrus ivory, five pieces

English (?); middle of the twelfth century

h 18·5 cm w 14 cm

Musée du Louvre, Paris

Beckwith, *op cit* no 87; Lasko, *Ars Sacra*, p. 172

The Latin inscriptions identify the Hand of God at the head of the cross, Sun and Moon on the arms and at the base a kneeling patroness (?) Sibylla.

A walrus ivory relief carved with a representation of the Crucifixion in the Landesmuseum, Darmstadt (No. 501) mounted on a fourteenth-century bookcover decorated with enamels from the workshop of Godefroi de Claire, dating from the middle of the twelfth century, has been considered to be related to the piece above, not because of style which is palpably different, but because the manuscript, an Evangelistary dating from the middle of the twelfth century, contains a portrait with an inscription identifying a certain Sibylla. The manuscript formerly belonged to the Church of St Gereon in Cologne. Two ladies have been suggested as possible patrons: Abbess Sibylla of Flanders (d. 1157) and Sibylla, wife of Count Dietrich of Flanders, who died in Jerusalem as Abbess of the Lazarus Convent in 1163. The latter was well known as a benefactress to the Church. Since the style of the carvings is so different and Sibylla was a fairly common name in the eleventh and twelfth centuries it seems preferable to accept two totally different workshops and possibly a difference of date.

49

The Deposition

Ivory

English (School of Herefordshire);
about 1150

h 21·5 cm *w* 12 cm

Victoria and Albert Museum, London
no 3–1872

Beckwith, *op cit* no 88

From the Webb Collection

The style of the relief should be
compared to sculpture in the west
country at Kilpeck, Leominster, and
Castle Frome, to a door-knocker at
Dormington, and to manuscripts in the
Cathedral Library at Hereford.

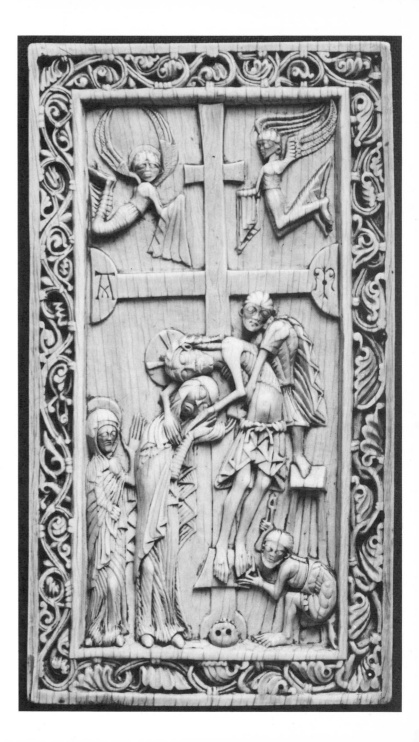

50

Two Pierced Reliefs

Bone

English (possibly Winchester);
second quarter of the twelfth century

h 22·5 cm w 13·5 cm
h 21·5 cm w 13 cm

Victoria and Albert Museum, London
no 8461 A & B 1863

Beckwith, *op cit* no 89

Formerly mounted on the covers of a
Bible printed in Paris in 1552.
Acquired in London.

Professor Dr Otto Pächt has suggested
verbally that the ornament on these
reliefs should be compared with that
in the second Winchester Bible
(Oxford, Bodl.Ms.Auct.E.inf.1)
illuminated at Winchester between
1140 and 1150. He also suggested the
hypothesis that the reliefs were
originally the cover of the Shaftesbury
Psalter (Brit.Mus.Lansdowne 383).

51

Head of a Tau-Cross*

Walrus ivory

English (School of Winchester);
middle of the twelfth century

h 5·5 cm l 16·5 cm

Victoria and Albert Museum, London
no 371–1871

Beckwith, *op cit* no 91

On one side Christ Pantocrator
between St Michael subduing a dragon
and a man trapped in the jaws of a
serpent; on the other side the Virgin
and child flanked by men trapped in
the jaws of serpents.

Formerly in the collections of Piot and
of Baron de Crassier at Liège. From the
Webb Collection.

According to an old ascription the
tau-cross was formerly in the
Cathedral at Liège, but the Treasury
was not apparently sold until 1794–
1795, and in 1715, if not before, the
tau-cross was already in the collection
of Baron de Crassier at Liège who,
according to Piot, was at this date in
communication with de Montfaucon
concerning it. An almost identical tau-cross in the Basilewsky collection at
the Hermitage is apparently a recent
copy. With the tau-head must go the
centre of another in the British
Museum (Beckwith, *op cit* no 92)
which would appear to be by the same
hand. A bronze-gilt censer top in the
British Museum also shows many
points of resemblance; it was found in
the Thames near London Bridge.

52

An Arm from a Stool

Not exhibited

Walrus ivory

English (School of Winchester);
middle of the twelfth century

l 58 cm *h* of middle 4·2 cm

Museo Nazionale, Florence
Carrand No. 47

Beckwith, *op cit* no 93

On one side the symbol of St Mark;
on the other the symbol of St John.

Traces of gilding. Slight breaks. On the
under side, in the middle, a rectangular
depression (2 cm × 1·3 cm) for
conjunction with another part of the
stool.

Formerly in the Meyricke and
Carrand Collections

53

Head of a crozier

Walrus ivory

English (School of Winchester);
middle of the twelfth century

h 15 cm Diameter of knop 4·5 cm

Musée de Cluny, Paris

Beckwith, *op cit* no 94

Formerly in the Spitzer and Carrand
Collections.

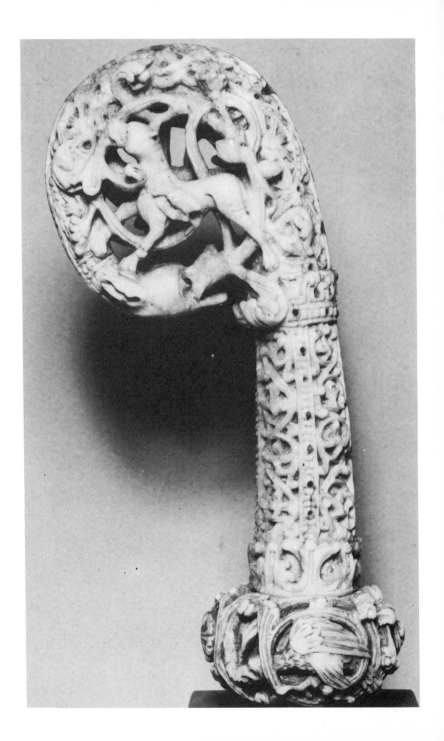

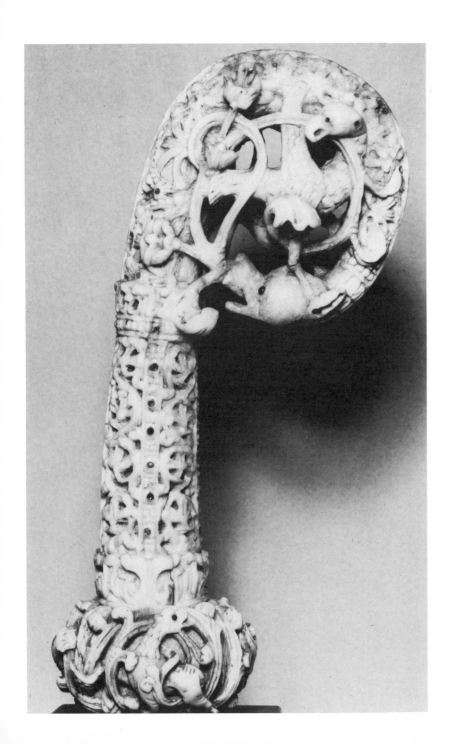

54

Head of a crozier *

Walrus ivory

English (School of Winchester);
middle of the twelfth century

h 17·5 cm *w* 6·5 cm

Museo Nazionale, Florence
Carrand No. 45

Beckwith, *op cit* no 95

Formerly in the Carrand Collection.

55

The St Nicholas Crozier

Ivory

Illustrated on front cover

English (School of Canterbury); about 1180

h 12 cm *w* 11 cm

Victoria and Albert Museum, London no 218–1865

Beckwith, *op cit* no 98

From the Webb Collection

On one side, scenes from the Nativity of Christ; on the other side, scenes from the life of St Nicholas.

The eyes were inlaid with jet or paste. Missing are the *Agnus Dei*, the head of the middle daughter of the indigent nobleman and the right hand of St Nicholas. The absence of the hand of Salome is probably explained by the

legend that her hand withered when she touched the manger because she refused to believe in the Divinity of the Child.

It is probable that the crozier was carved for Archbishop Richard of Canterbury (1173–1184) whose tomb was discovered between 1735 and 1740 in the north aisle of the cathedral.

56

The Ascension*

Ivory

English (School of Canterbury);
about 1180

h 13·6 cm w 7·6 cm

Victoria and Albert Museum, London
no A 15–1955

Beckwith, *op cit* no 99

Acquired in Paris from Dr M. R. Allard. Nothing is known of the provenance of the relief which is said to have been in the possession of Madame Allard's family 'depuis un temps immémorial'.

57

The Rest on the Flight into Egypt

Ivory

English (School of Canterbury);
about 1180

h 7·8 cm *w* 3·9 cm

The Metropolitan Museum of Art,
New York Dodge Fund, 40.62

Beckwith, *op cit* no 100; S. Schwartz,
'Symbolic Allusions in a Twelfth-
Century Ivory'. *Marsyas* XVI. 1972–73,
p. 36ff.

The eyes are inlaid with jet or black
paste. The fragmentary condition of
the relief precludes a reconstruction of
its original appearance and context.

Formerly in the collection of Monsieur
Em.Théodore at Lille.
Exhibited at Tournai in 1911.

58

Naked men and salamanders

Walrus ivory capital

English (School of Canterbury);
about 1180–1190

w 5·4 cm *Depth* 3·1 cm

British Museum, London

Beckwith, *op cit* no 101

Probably part of a flabellum handle.
Formerly in the Maskell Collection.
Acquired in 1856.

59

**Scenes of Biblical Sacrifice
and Offering**

Bone

English (School of Canterbury ?);
second half of the twelfth century

h 20·3 cm *w* 9·8 cm

Merseyside County Museums,
Liverpool

Beckwith, *op cit* no 102

Formerly in the Mayer Collection
(No. 34)

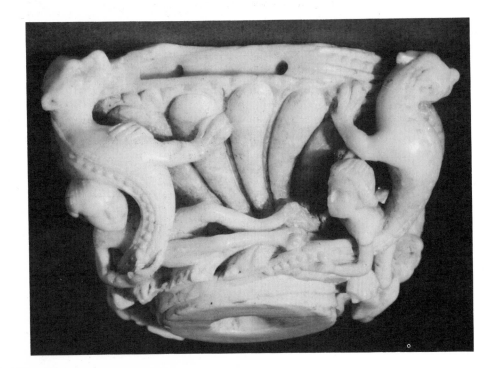

Reading from top to bottom: Moses
receives the Law; the Sacrifice of
Isaac; the Presentation in the Temple;
the Offering of the Paschal Lamb;
Melchisidech offers bread and wine.
Traces of green pigmentation. It is
possible that the eyes were inlaid with
jet or black paste. Possibly a book-
cover but considering the two
rectangular cavities on the right edge
probably a lid of a casket.

60

Fragment of a Crucifix⋆

Walrus ivory

English (School of Canterbury ?);
late twelfth century

h 13·5 cm

Guildhall Museum, London.

Beckwith, *op cit* no 103

Traces of gilding

Found in Worship Street in the City
of London.

61

A Cross

Walrus ivory

English (Bury St Edmunds?
Canterbury?); 1180–1190

h 57·7 cm w 36·2 cm

The Metropolitan Museum of Art,
New York
The Cloisters Collection, Nos. 63.12;
63.127

Beckwith, *op cit* no 104; Lasko, *Ars
Sacra*, p. 167 argues for a date in the
early twelfth century.

On the front a tree with several
branches is attached to the frame of
the cross. At the intersection of the
arms a central medallion supported by
four angels contains St Peter pointing
to the figure of Christ and holding a
scroll with a text from Acts,x,43
stating that to Him all the prophets
bore witness; just above St Peter,
St John holds aloft a scroll with a text
from John,iii,14 stating that as Moses
lifted up the serpent in the wilderness,
even so must the Son of Man be lifted
up, – and turns his head round to look
at the scene behind him where Moses
brandishes another scroll with a text
from Deuteronomy,xxviii,66 stating
that 'thy life shall hang in doubt
before thee' in front of the Brazen
Serpent raised up on a forked stick
and surrounded by eight Israelites; at
the top of the medallion a figure lies

supine with his head twisted round to look at the scene below and holding a scroll with a text from Jeremiah,xiv,9, 'why shouldst thou be as a wandering man, as a mighty man that cannot save?'; below right on the other side of Moses is Isaiah bending slightly and holding a scroll with a text from Isaiah,lxiii,2 'wherefore art thou red in thine apparel and thy garments like him that treadeth in the winevat?'.

At the end of the right arm a panel is carved with the Deposition and the Lamentation. In the latter scene Zachariah mourns over the head of Christ and holds a scroll with a text from Zachariah, xii, 10, 'and they shall mourn for him as one mourning for an only son' – floating over four skulls indicating Golgotha. At the end of the left arm a panel is carved with the Resurrection and the Maries at the Sepulchre; in the latter scene the Angel of the Resurrection points to a scroll with a text from St Mark,xvi,6 'You seek Jesus of Nazareth who was crucified.' At the head of the cross the Hand of God emerges from a cloud beneath the *titulus* on which is written in Greek, Latin and pseudo-Hebrew characters: Jesus of Nazareth, King *of those who confess*. Above the *titulus* stand the High Priest Caiaphas and Pontius Pilate, Caiaphas pointing to Pilate and holding a scroll with a text from St John,xix,21 'Write not The King of the Jews but that he said, I am King of the Jews' while Pilate points at the *titulus* with one hand and in the other holds a scroll with a text from St. John,xix,22: 'What I have written

I have written.' Above these figures, the Ascension with Christ disappearing into the clouds and below the clouds two angels with scrolls bearing texts from Acts 1, ii 'Men of Galilee, why do you stand gazing up into heaven?' and 'He shall so come in like manner as you have seen him go into heaven.'

On the narrow sides and top of the Ascension panel are three Greek words: Anthropos (Man), Christ, Pantocrator. The panel at the foot of the cross represents Christ before Caiaphas; the scroll bears the word 'Prophecy' referring to St Matthew, xxvi,68 'Prophecy unto us, thou Christ, who is he that smote thee?' Immediately above this plaque, Adam, holding a scroll bearing the

letter A, and Eve. On either side of the knotted tree course inscriptions referring to the Resurrection and the inadequacy of the Synagogue and on the narrow side of the cross referring to Ham's derision on seeing his naked father and the derision of the Jews before the dying Christ. On the back of the cross the central medallion, supported by angels contains the Agnus Dei pierced by the Synagogue who holds a scroll with a text from Deuteronomy,xxi,23 'He that is hanged upon the tree is accursed of God'; behind St John weeps, identified by an inscription from Apocalypse, v,4 'John: and I wept much.' Opposite him, hovering within the medallion, an archangel points to a scroll which passes over the head of St John and bears texts from Apocalypse,v,5

and v,12. 'Weep not, behold. Worthy is the Lamb that was slain to receive virtue and divinity'; beneath the lamb is the bust of Jeremiah holding a scroll with a text from Jeremiah,xi,19 'I was like a lamb that is brought to the slaughter'; on the top of the medallion the same prophet reclines holding a scroll with a continuation from the verse xi,19 'Let us cut him off from the land of the living.' At the head of the cross is the symbol of St John the Evangelist carrying a scroll on which is the text from St John,xix,37 – 'They shall look on him whom they pierced' and xix,36 'A bone of him shall not be broken'; at the end of the left arm, the symbol of St Mark, at the end of the right arm the symbol of St Luke; at the foot of the cross the symbol of St Matthew is missing. Below the symbol

of St John the sequence of prophets, each identified and holding scrolls with texts from their books, starts with David and ends with Job (cf. Beckwith, *op cit* no 104).

The cross is made up from seven pieces of walrus ivory fitted together by tongues of ivory which slip into sheaths and are secured by pegs, The panel representing Christ before Caiaphas was in a private collection in Berlin in 1932. Several holes indicate

the position of the original figure of Christ which is almost certainly No. 62.

Formerly in the Topić Mimara Collection.

An attempt to assign the cross to Bury St Edmunds on the grounds of the anti-Jewish flavour of the inscriptions has been undermined by the fact that anti-Jewish feeling was rampant in England in the second half of the twelfth century. The cross is an anthology of prophetic and Gospel texts and the combination of literary text and complex, rather cramped illustration is certainly a characteristic of early medieval art in England. The knotted cross is known in Anglo-Saxon illumination but it becomes an almost constant factor in thirteenth and fourteenth century English manuscripts, embroideries and an occasional ivory and alabaster carving. The style is a development of the workshop mannerisms of the middle of the twelfth century and comes closer in atmosphere with the late Canterbury carvings: Nos. 55, 56, 57, 58, 59. The drapery of the little figures on the cross should also be considered with a small stone fragment from Bridlington Priory, now in the Victoria and Albert Museum, which has been dated between 1170 and 1180; the scroll-bearing prophets should be compared to those on stone capitals, dating about 1190, on the west front of Dunstable Priory, Bedfordshire.

62

Fragment of a Crucifix

Walrus ivory

English (Canterbury?); about 1180–1190

h 19 cm

Kunstindustrimuseet, Oslo

Beckwith, *op cit* no 105

Formerly in the collection of Professor Emil Hannover at Copenhagen. This figure may well belong to No. 61.

63

Aaron's Rod

Walrus ivory

English (Canterbury?);
late twelfth century

h 5·4 cm w 5 cm

Museo Nazionale, Florence
Carrand 72

Beckwith, *op cit* no 106

The inscription identifies the figure.
Inlaid with jet or paste.
Formerly in the collections of Ed.
Barry, Toulouse, and Carrand, Lyons.
Exhibited in Paris in 1867.

64

Reliquary Cross

Ivory

English; late twelfth century (?)

h 7·2 cm *w* 5·7 cm

Mr John Hunt

Beckwith, *op cit* no 108; Lasko, *Ars Sacra*, p. 167, in company with the owner, prefers a date in the late eleventh century.

On the front Christ on the Cross; above the head of Christ the Hand of God. On the back the *Agnus Dei* surrounded by the symbols of the Evangelists.

The eyes are inlaid with jet or paste.

Formerly in the Collection of Countess S. Bernstorff Gyldensteen.

Index